The Beaver Book of
BRAIN TICKLERS

Charles Booth-Jones

Illustrated by Michael Jackson and Lesley Smith

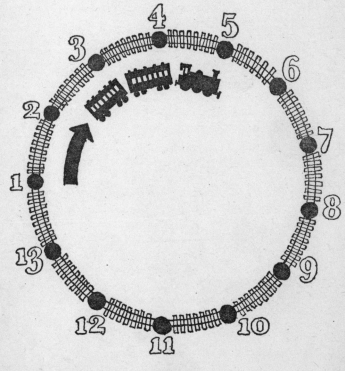

Beaver Books

First published in 1977 by
The Hamlyn Publishing Group Limited
London · New York · Sydney · Toronto
Astronaut House, Feltham, Middlesex, England

© Copyright Text Charles Booth-Jones 1977
© Copyright Illustrations
The Hamlyn Publishing Group Limited 1977
ISBN 0 600 31396 4

Printed in England by
Cox and Wyman Limited
London, Reading and Fakenham
Set in Monotype Garamond

Contents

Acknowledgement

The author and publishers would like to thank Invicta Plastics Limited for kindly allowing us to base problem 87 (page 68) on the game Mastermind which is their copyright.

1 Triangles

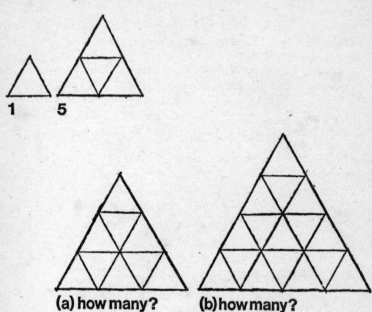

1   5

(a) how many?   (b) how many?

2 A Striking Problem

Our hall clock has a simple striker. At 4 o'clock it strikes four times, at 4.30 it strikes once, at 5 o'clock it strikes five times, at 5.30 it strikes once, and so on.

Last night I went to sleep early. When I awoke it was still very dark. I heard the clock strike once, but I could not tell what time it was. Half an hour later it struck once again, but I still could not tell what time it was. After a further half hour it again struck once. *Then* I knew what time it was, and I immediately fell asleep.

What time was it when I did at last fall asleep?

3 Noughts and Crosses

In the game shown, where will you put your mark to be sure of winning,
  (*a*) if your mark is O?
  (*b*) if your mark is X?
In each case give the number of the square.

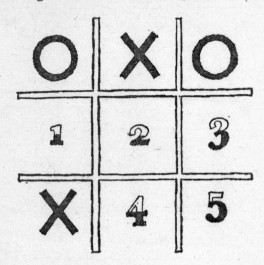

4 Collision Course

Two sets of model railway tracks cross each other at four points. The black dots on the diagram divide the track into equal sections.

Two tank engines start at the same moment, a black one from the point A, and a white one from any of the eight points on its own track. Arrows show the direction of travel of the engines. They both travel at exactly the same speed.

(*a*) If the white engine starts from the point Z, where will it collide with the black engine?

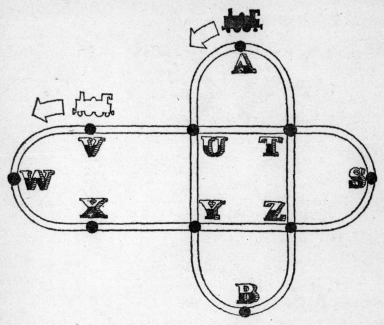

(*b*) Where should the white engine start from in order to collide with the black engine at the point Y:

    (i) after as *short* a time as possible?

    (ii) after as *long* a time as possible?

(*c*) Why can the engines never collide at the point T?

5 Coloured Numbers

If all ODD numbers are *red* and all EVEN numbers are *blue*, what colour is *red added to blue*?

6 Suicide Squad

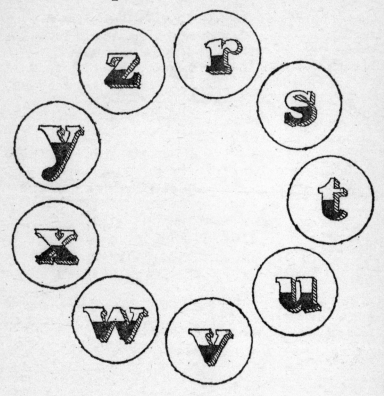

Here are the nine members of the 'Death-before-surrender Commando' about to die by their own hands rather than give in to the enemy. They are standing in a ring facing each other.

Starting with their commander at R, each man will shoot the one on his left when his turn comes – if he is still left alive! The last man alive will then shoot himself.

Corporal C. Custard has other ideas. He decides to *be* the last man – and stay alive!

Where should he stand in the circle of death?

7 Number Wheels

These 'wheels' each have one blank space to be filled in. As an example, the answer in the centre wheel is 8, because this fits into the run 2, 4, 6, ... 10. None of the missing numbers is 0, but one of the wheels has two possible answers.

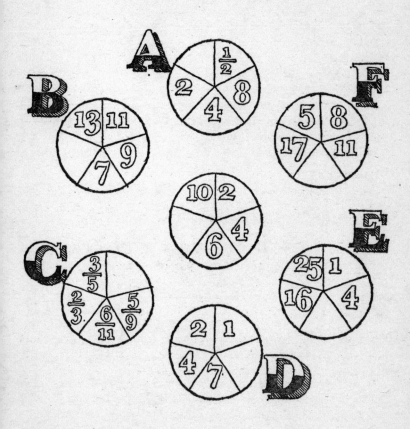

8 The Sultan's Choice

Here is a simpler version of a time-honoured problem.

The Sultan wanted to choose a new minister, the last one having panicked, or 'lost his head'. There were two candidates for the post.

'Here are three discs,' said the Sultan, 'two white and one black. I shall pin one of these on each of your backs, so that you can only see each other's disc. There you are,' he said, pinning a white disc on each man's back, 'now go into the next room. The first one who comes and tells me what coloured disc he is wearing will be my Chief Minister, and his first job will be to execute the other man.'

After a couple of minutes one man came out and correctly told the Sultan that he was wearing a white disc. 'How did you work it out?' asked the Sultan.

What was his reply?

9 Which Numbers?

Excavating in the ruins of the ancient capital city of the Pheno-Barbitone civilisation, Professor J. Bones came across a school-boy's tablet on which was inscribed the cryptic line of writing shown:

It is known that in Pheno-Barbarian writing T stands for 'multiplied by' and W for 'equals'; also that the Triangle, Square and Circle are each symbols for (different) single-figure numbers such as 7.

Can you suggest what numbers each of the three symbols could stand for? (In fact, there are several sets of possible numbers.)

10 Compass Square

Mr North, Mr East, Mr South and Mr West each live on a different side of Compass Square. Curiously enough, no one lives on the same side as his own name, e.g., Mr East does not live on the east side.

Mr South lives further east than Mr North, while Mr North does not live further west than Mr West.

On which side of the square does Mr East live?

11 Sum Code

Did you know that six and six can add together to make nine? They do in the addition sum below, because each of the five letters E, I, N, S and X stands for a different one of the numerals 1, 2, 3, up to 9.

```
      S I X
  +   S I X
    N I N E
```

Can you work out what number the word INNS stands for?

12 On the Buses

Service 1001 runs every 10 minutes between Boothmouth Pier and the Park. Buses wait at the Pier for 5 minutes before returning.

At 11 AM Arthur is driving a bus which is due to reach the Pier at 11.15. When will he pass his friend Bill who is driving the bus ahead of him?

13 Join the Points

There are twelve points marked round this circle, some of them joined to each other by straight lines. How many straight lines would be needed to join every point to every other point?

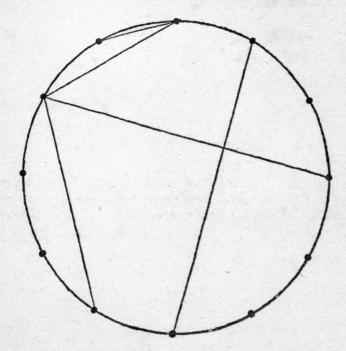

14 A Bowling Problem

We have a set of five plastic bowls, all of different sizes. They all stack neatly inside each other. For instance, size 3 will fit inside size 4 or size 5, but not inside size 2 or size 1.

Yesterday, when drying the dishes, I found myself holding in my left hand the size 4 bowl with size 2 inside it. The other bowls were already stacked in the cupboard, and I had to add these to the pile. How did I do it?

(As usual in our kitchen, there were no empty spaces to put the bowls down on.)

15 Squares

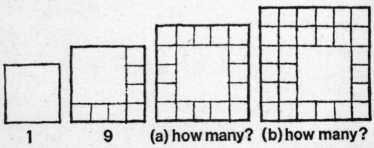

1   9   (a) how many?   (b) how many?

16 Double Bullseye

What are X and Y?

And, by the way, where do the sequences of numbers come from?

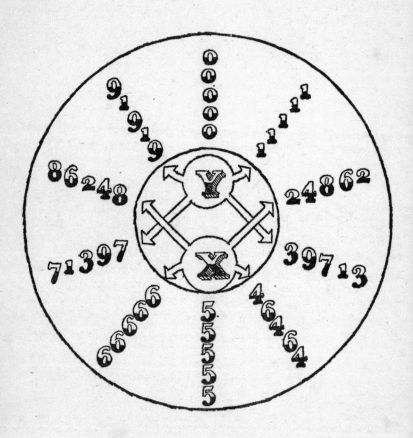

17 Racing News

Alan, Bill and Colin were the only three competitors to finish in the 10-kilometres dash. I asked them about the result afterwards, and each made two statements. Unfortunately, one of the boys lied in both his statements, but the others told the truth, so I was able to tell who came in which place.

Alan said, 'I was first, Colin was last.'
Bill said, 'Alan was not first, Colin was second.'
Colin said, 'I beat Alan, Bill was not second.'
What was the result of the race?

18 Target

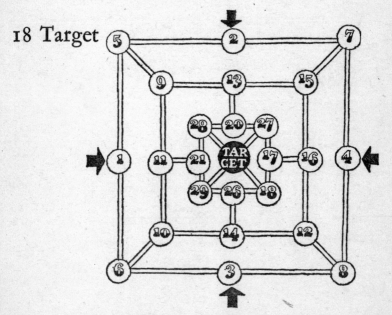

Here is a simple game to play. You enter the system by one of the arrows, and proceed by the lines until you reach the target. Every time you pass through one of the circles you score the points shown in that circle.

What is the smallest total of points needed to reach the target?

19 League Table

Here is the final position in our inter-village 'Friendly' Football Championship for this season:

TEAM	POINTS
PUNCHAM	5
KICKHAM	3
TRIPHAM	3
FOULHAM	1

As usual, a win gained 2 points and a draw 1 point.

Every team played every other team once. Kickham were the only team not beaten by Puncham. Two teams never won a match.

Can you give the results of the three matches played by Tripham?

20 Drink Problem

A full bottle of Dopa-Zola costs 25p. If the drink inside costs 20p more than the bottle containing it, how much does the empty bottle cost?

21 Brick-work

Here are three (identical) toy bricks from a set I saw in a shop window recently. I thought they were rather unusual, so I bought them for my small nephew.

Can you say, from what you see, which faces are opposite to each other? The six designs are circle, square, cross, star, dot and an all-black face.

22 Pentagon

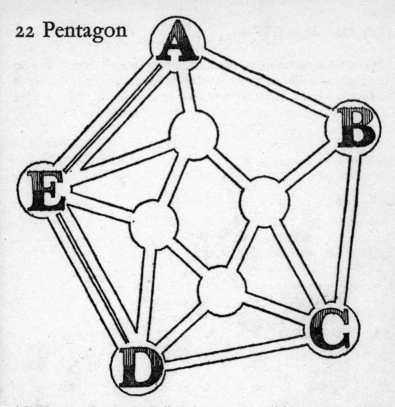

The famous Pentagon Gallery has an unusual layout as you can see from the plan. The circles represent rooms, the lines corridors. All the pictures are in the corridors. There are five entrances, shown at rooms A, B, C, D and E. Some of the rooms are connected by two corridors, as you can see. I find it takes me on average about 10 minutes to 'do' each corridor – I spend no time at all in the actual rooms themselves.

If I want to see every corridor and take as short a time as possible (not passing through any corridor more than once if I can manage it)

(a) where should I go in?
(b) where should I come out?
(c) how long should it take me?

23 Round Trip

Our local island railway system has only one train, which runs clockwise round all the 13 stations (they are numbered). If you miss the train you just have to wait until it comes round again! It takes 10 minutes per station, so it's an 130-minute wait.

In future, to economise on fuel in starting and stopping, the train will miss out every four stations. So, when it starts at station No 1, its next stop is No 6, then No 11, then No 3, and so on. However, by cutting time spent at stations and running faster, it will still take 10 minutes per station (e.g., from No 1 to No 6).

My own station is No 5. I often have to go to No 3 on business. Will the new system get me there more quickly than the old one, or less, and what will be the difference? Also, what about the return journey from No 3 to No 5?

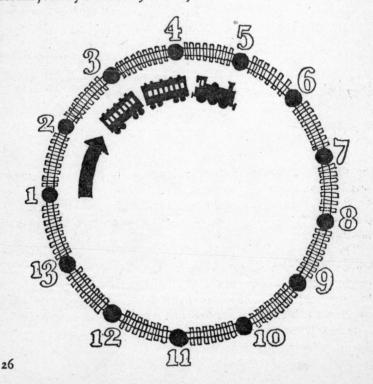

24 Watch Out!

The face of my watch is marked in three different ways: the minutes are numbered 5, 10, 15, and so on up to 60; the hours are marked 1, 2, 3, and so on up to 12; and the hours are also marked for the 24-hour clock, e.g., 6 o'clock is also marked 18 o'clock.

Is the minute marking and the 24-hour clock marking the same at any point on the dial?

25 Rectangles

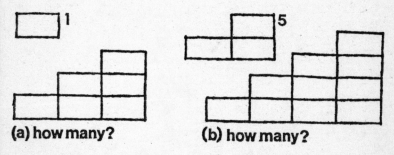

(a) how many?

(b) how many?

26 Waxwork

At the Boothmouth Waxworks until recently stood the solid wax life-size figure of the town's most famous son, General Jonas O'Booth. After the General's court-martial for opening fire on a passing shooting star, it was decided to melt down the 2-metre tall figure.

The 'General O'Booth Fan Club', all eight members of it, sprang fiercely into action. They demanded that the wax from the original statue be used to make smaller solid wax versions, one for each member to keep. To avoid an ugly situation this was done, every drop of the original wax being used in the process.

How tall was each of the smaller statues?

27 Guess the Pattern

A	B	C	D	E
C	A	D	BC	E
	CD	A		CE
BD		C	A	DE
?	?	?	?	?

Here is a grid of 25 spaces into which the letters A, B, C, D and E have been fitted. Each of these five letters has been positioned according to a different pattern.

Can you fill in the bottom line? (Each of the question marks may stand for one or more letters or for a blank space.)

28 Tangled Ages

There are four boys in the Noel family, all of different ages, but all with the same birthday – Christmas Day! I get very confused over their ages.

I do remember that John is over 15, while George is over 10. Bill is a year younger than George, and Tim's age is between Bill's and John's.

The other day I discovered that John is now 16. I also know that George's and John's birthdays are 3 years apart.

Yes, I have to agree it's all rather confusing, but all the same, what can you find out about Tim's age?

29 What Shape ?

What shape goes in place of the question mark?

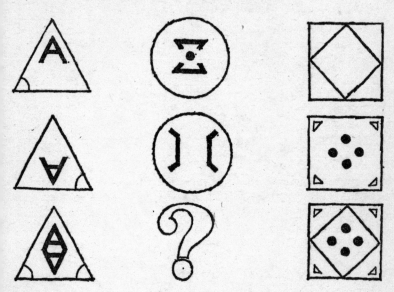

30 Cut the Cards

The other day I needed some rectangular cards each 20 centimetres by 12 centimetres for my filing system. I thought it would perhaps be cheaper to make my own from large rectangular sheets. The only suitable ones I could buy measured 60 centimetres by 45 centimetres.

How many cards was I able to cut out of each sheet?

31 Money Mad

Last year I went on holiday to Lunatavia. I found their money system quite mad.

Of course, they have 100-Luna notes, but smaller amounts have to be made up using the coins shown – there are *no* other values!

Some amounts, such as 1 or 4 or 11 Lunas, just can't be made up using these coins. Naturally, one can sometimes manage by getting change, but to make up difficult amounts exactly Gold Shield Stamps can be used – what a system! However, as a Lunative friend of mine explained, the stamps are *not* allowed to be used for an amount such as 14 or 18 Lunas, because these can be made up by coins alone.

What is the largest amount for which Gold Shield Stamps *can* be used to help?

32 Topo-bricks

These are plastic cubes, coloured white on top, red on the bottom, and blue on the four side faces. They fit together by means of small connectors in the centres of the blue faces.

How many different white shapes can you make with four bricks? Draw your results like this:

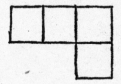

Also, put a ring round any of your examples which would cease to be different from any of the others if the bottom face of each Topo-brick was coloured white like the top face.

33 Weird Numbers

If 6 is written 1, 10 is written 0, and 23 is written 3, what answers would you write under these sums?

$$+\frac{3}{4}$$

$$\times\frac{3}{4}$$

$$-\frac{3}{4}$$

34 The Truth Game

If these three statements are true:

ALL DONKEYS HAVE LONG EARS

NONE OF MY AUNTS IS A DONKEY

SOME OF MY AUNTS DRINK CIDER

Then which one of these statements below
  (*a*) *must* be true (X, Y or Z)?
  (*b*) *might* be true (X, Y or Z)?
  (*c*) *cannot* be true (X, Y or Z)?

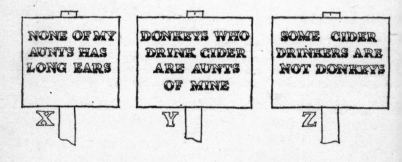

NONE OF MY AUNTS HAS LONG EARS

DONKEYS WHO DRINK CIDER ARE AUNTS OF MINE

SOME CIDER DRINKERS ARE NOT DONKEYS

X

Y

Z

35 More Triangles

(from an idea suggested by Jonathan Page)

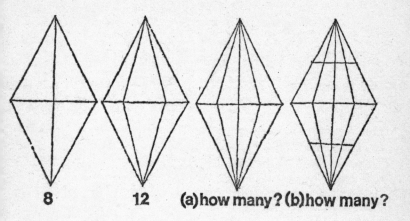

8　　　　**12**　　　　**(a)how many? (b)how many?**

36 Handy Angles

About when (to the nearest minute in each case) between the hours of 7 and 8 o'clock are the hour and minute hands of your watch

(*a*) on top of each other?

(*b*) at right angles to each other?

(*c*) opposite to each other?

37 Rolling Dice

This is a 'normal' die, that is to say each pair of opposite faces carry numbers which add up to 7.

Sketch the die in three positions, arrived at successively as follows:

(a) roll it a quarter turn clockwise (so that the bottom face turns up on the left side)

(b) roll the resulting die a quarter turn towards you (so that the back face arrives on top)

(c) rotate the resulting die a quarter turn (so that the left-hand face goes to the back).

38 Dice Again

These two (identical) dice have been placed side by side so that the faces touching each other are the same.

One of the faces shown in the diagram has a question mark. What number should be marked on this face instead of ? ?

39 Odd and Even

The Sultan was testing a candidate for the post of Court Mathematician.

'I am thinking, O Ali, of two numbers, one of them odd, the other even. I now multiply my first number by an *even* number. Then I multiply my second number by an *odd* number. Finally, I add the two results together. The answer is *odd*.

'Tell me now, O Wise One, was my first number odd or even? Think well. If you are successful, the post is yours. If not, my executioner will bisect you at right angles.'

Assuming Ali kept his head, what was his reply, and why?

40 Black and White Cars

The famous B–J Midgi-cars are either black and 4 centimetres long or white and 7 centimetres long:

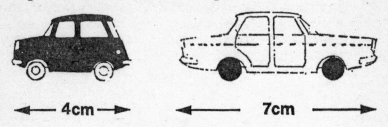

← **4cm** → ← **7cm** →

They are supplied in boxes of different lengths, like this, for example:

← **30cm** →

The other day my shop was supplied with one box 34 centimetres long and one box 29 centimetres long.

How many black and how many white Midgi-cars were there altogether in the two boxes?

41 A Look into the Future

1st January 2051 will be a Sunday. What is the next year in which 1st January will again be a Sunday?

1st January 2052 will be a Monday. What is the next year in which 1st January will again be a Monday?

42 Breakfast Menu

Form 9A at school recently were given the task of carrying out a survey to discover what other members of the school liked to eat for breakfast at home. Here are the results of their findings for Form 7Z:

LIKES	NUMBER OF CHILDREN
Porridge only (it was winter)	2
Bacon only	5
Eggs only	6
Porridge and bacon	7
Bacon and eggs	5
Eggs and porridge	4
TOTAL NUMBER OF CHILDREN IN FORM 7Z	21

I didn't like their adding up much. Then it was realised that they had failed to ask every question they needed for their results – some of the children liked porridge, bacon *and* eggs. Can you find out how many?

43 Parallelograms

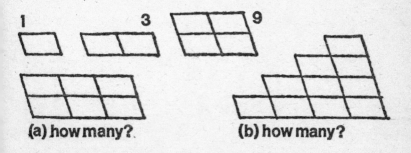

(a) how many?   (b) how many?

44 Cyclo-cross

Our local version of this popular sport allows a choice of roads or cross-country paths, or a mixture of both.

Above is a sketch of the permitted routes with distances (in kilometres) and check-points (lettered). Roads are shown in full lines, cross-country paths in dotted lines.

Starting at A, you *must* clock in at C, finishing at G. Which other check-points you visit depends on which route you choose. I calculate that 1 kilometre across country is equivalent to 5 kilometres by road (i.e. that both take the same travelling time).

Which routes shall I follow, and how many *kilometres by road* is this equivalent to?

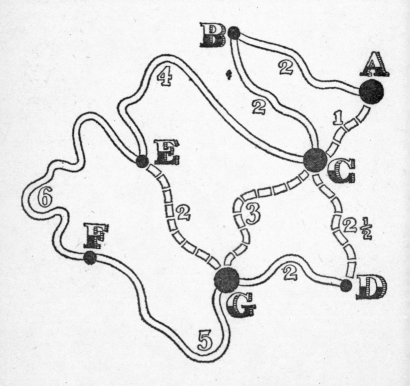

45 A Tartan Problem

Here is the somewhat unusual tartan of the Old Thousandth Foot ('The Black and White Highlanders'). It is constructed to a secret formula invented by the founder of the Regiment, Mad Major Mulligatawny MacJones, just before (some say, just after) he retired to the Regimental Asylum:

Can you say what shading or shadings (if any) should go in each of the two squares marked A and B?

46 Bomb Scare

Professor ('The Fiend') Moriarty has decided to blow up the Town Hall in protest against the rejection of his plan to suspend a bypass *over* the town from balloons. The bomb mechanism will be started up at 9 AM on Friday the 13th. The special triggering device is as follows: two lamps both showing green are connected together; when either lamp turns *from RED to GREEN* it changes the colour of the other one – either from red to green, or from green to red as the case may be; this changeover process takes 10 seconds.

Both lamps start at green. Then the left-hand one is changed automatically in colour every minute. When *both* lamps next show green together for half a minute, the bomb goes off.

When will the bomb explode?

47 Seating Problem

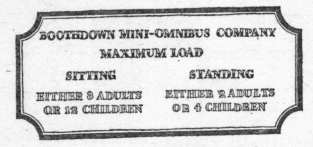

BOOTHDOWN MINI-OMNIBUS COMPANY

MAXIMUM LOAD

SITTING   STANDING

EITHER 8 ADULTS   EITHER 2 ADULTS
OR 12 CHILDREN   OR 4 CHILDREN

As driver/conductor of a one-man mini-omnibus, I have to enforce the seating regulations. As you can see, they *look* clear enough, but are they?

The other day my only passengers were 7 children, all comfortably seated. Then we came to the village of Lower Boothing. It was raining heavily and 6 adults wanted to get in.

The question is, how many of them could I let on the bus, and still keep to the regulations?

48 The Dancing Men
(*with apologies to Mr Sherlock Holmes*)

The last time we went on holiday we left our dogs in the care of a kind, but eccentric friend. He promised to send us a progress report after the first week. So he did – in code!!

Here is the message: can you decipher it? (I forgot to say that he was also looking after another pet of ours.)

49 Kitchen Tiles
(*from an idea suggested by Jonathan Page*)

When Mother complained that the tiles on her kitchen floor were cold to stand on, Father had a brain-wave – making use of the two spare mats which were in the loft to cover the tiles. Now, the kitchen floor has 90 square tiles, each of side half a metre. The mats measure 4 by $2\frac{1}{2}$ metres and 3 by $3\frac{1}{2}$ metres respectively. They looked like this:

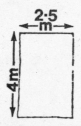
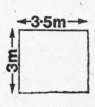

Of course, Father realised that the mats would not cover the whole floor, and would have to overlap, and could not be folded. Of course, also, he got things muddled, and ended by covering *as few* tiles as possible! Mother had to put things right, by rearranging the mats so as to cover *as many* tiles as possible.

How many tiles did Father manage to cover, and how many did Mother cover?

50 Tri-dominoes

These are thin, white plastic triangles, all three sides of which measure 3 centimetres. Any side of one Tri-domino will slot against any side of another so that they become connected. Both faces are identical, so that they can be turned over and still look the same.

Here are the only shapes you can make using two or three Tri-dominoes:

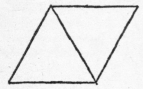 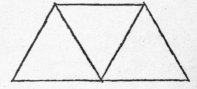

How many *different* shapes can you make using four or five Tri-dominoes?

51 Murder!

Inspector Sherlock Jones had four suspects for the killing. When he interviewed them, each made two statements. From his infra-red lie detector he knew that each man made *one true* and *one false* statement. As a result, he soon found his murderer. Can you?

A said, 'I did not do it. B did.'
B said, 'A did not do it. C did.'
C said, 'B did not do it. I did.'
D said, 'C did not do it. A did.'

52 International Date Line

This is longitude 180° – the opposite side of the world to longitude 0°, the Meridian of Greenwich.

Once upon a time (as in all fairy tales) I was sailing slowly westwards across the Pacific Ocean at 11 PM (local time) on Friday 13th of the month. Two hours later, after I had crossed the International Date Line, still sailing westwards, what time and date was it?

53 Cipher Message

From Agent 007, using a cipher grid of 25 squares numbered as shown. Each square of the grid can be referred to as a 2-figure number. As examples, square 32 (meaning 3 squares along and 2 down) and square 15 (meaning 1 square along and 5 down) have been marked in.

To prepare for enciphering or deciphering, start at square 11 and end at square 55, filling in the 25 letters of the alphabet (count I and J as the same letter). Begin with the code phrase of the week (no letter repeated), and then fill in the remaining letters of the alphabet in order.

This week the code phrase is 'BRAIN TICKLERS', and 007's message reads:

43 24 42 23 33 41 51 43 52 21 32 41 42 42 52 23
Can you decipher it?

54 Nim

This is the name usually given to an old game, probably of Chinese origin. Two players have several piles of counters between them. Each in turn can remove as many counters as he wants, but *only from one pile each turn*. The winner is the player who removes the last counter or counters from the board.

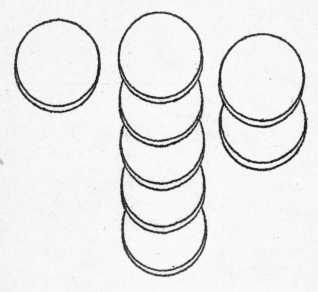

In the game shown, if it is your turn, from which pile will you remove one or more counters, and how many, in order to be sure of winning?

55 Circular Pattern

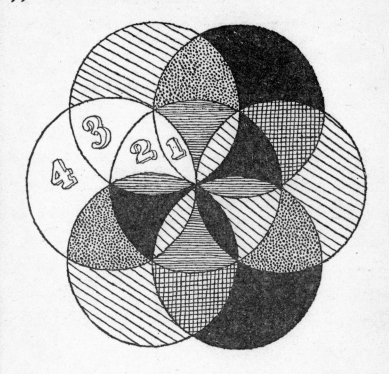

What shading should the parts of the pattern numbered 1, 2, 3 and 4 be?

56 Sweet Tooth

To keep me going each week I buy a number of packets of sweets, always of the same well-known brand.

Last week, for instance, I spent 19p on one packet of Boothmints, two of Boothgums and three of Boothjubes.

This week I've spent 25p on three packets of Boothmints, two of Boothgums and one of Boothjubes.

Next week, I'm afraid, I'll have to economise. I can only afford to buy one packet of each sort. How much will that cost me?

57 More Mad Money

This year, on holiday in Lunatavia again, I found that – for the benefit of British tourists – they had reformed their mad money system, the one I told you about in Problem 31. But is it an improvement?

There are four sorts of coins now, all different *shapes*! Instead of giving you their value in Lunas, each one tells you how many of the previous coin it is worth – what a system again! Here are the coins:

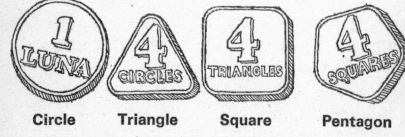

Circle   **Triangle**   **Square**   **Pentagon**

Of course, being Lunatavia, things were made more difficult than they need be. You see, to make up any given amount, you cannot use more than three coins of any one shape except the Pentagon, e.g., you can't use four or five or more Triangles.

Perhaps you'd like to try your hand at some of the problems I was faced with while on holiday:

(a) What *coins* did I get as change when I bought a 30-Luna scarf with 1 Pentagon?

(b) How did I manage to pay exactly for a 75-Luna bracelet?

(c) How many Lunas did it cost for a railway journey to Dimburg? I gave the man all my coins, and he selected 2 Squares, 3 Triangles and 1 Circle.

58 Trapeziums

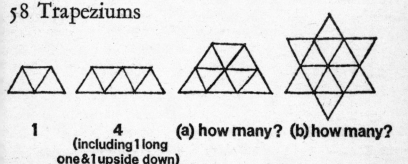

1   **4**   **(a) how many? (b) how many?**
(including 1 long
one & 1 upside down)

59 Age Differences

If the difference between Amanda's and Bruce's ages is 5 years, and the difference between Bruce's and Charlotte's ages is 5 years, and the difference between Charlotte's and Donald's ages is 5 years, then

(a) could Amanda be the same age as Donald?

(b) if Bruce is the youngest, could Donald be the eldest?

(c) could the combined ages of the girls equal the combined ages of the boys?

(d) what is the least possible age gap between eldest and youngest?

60 Jig-saws

Can you put each of these sets of pieces together to form a square? (The dotted lines are there just to give you an idea of the sizes of the pieces.)

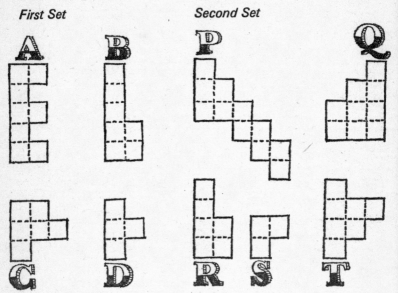

First Set   *Second Set*

61 Target Practice

Here is the sort of target we use on our miniature range, showing seven shots on it, each with a different score.

The other day four boys competed in a match. Each had five shots, so the highest possible points were 50 (5 'bulls'). The scores were:

GREEN 35
BROWN 41
WHITE 41
BLACK 48

I remember that Green's first two shots were 0 and 5. Brown's first shot was a bull, but his next three shots were all the same odd-numbered score. White had two pairs of even-numbered scores, ending with an odd number. Black, the crack shot, was disappointed when his last shot was a 9.

How many bulls were scored altogether?

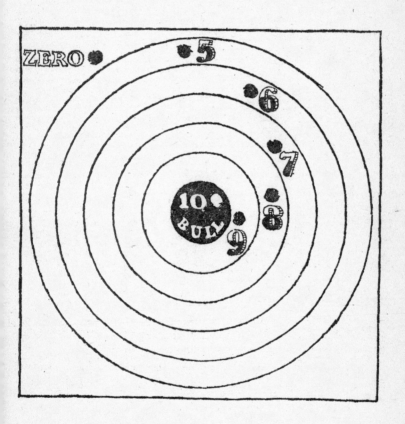

62 One to Twenty

This is the title of an old but simple game played by two people. Each in turn counts either 1 or 2 more on to the total reached so far. The winner is the player who reaches 20.

To begin, one player says either '1' or '2'. For example, if I start by saying '1', you could say '2' or '3'. Suppose you said '3', I could then say '4' or '5', and so on.

There is a way of making sure you win, provided you are allowed to start. Can you see how to do so?

63 Another Bomb Scare

In the corner of my bookshelf, as you see, I keep Professor B. Jones' famous compendium of knowledge in three volumes, each of 1000 pages.

My secretary, whom I had dismissed for eating ice-cream on duty, fitted up the books as a bomb while I was away on holiday.

The fuse ran from page 1 of Volume I to page 1000 of Volume III. It was timed to take 1 minute for each 1000 pages. The secretary needed 2 minutes to get away, so this 3-minute fuse should be safe enough, he reckoned.

Unfortunately the bomb blew up *before* the secretary escaped. Can you see why?

64 Regional Points

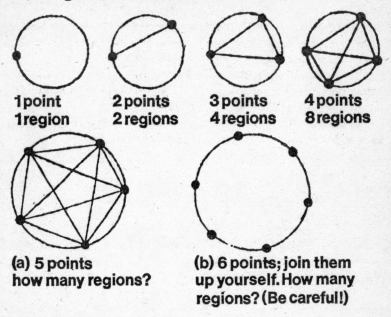

1 point
1 region

2 points
2 regions

3 points
4 regions

4 points
8 regions

(a) 5 points
how many regions?

(b) 6 points; join them
up yourself. How many
regions? (Be careful!)

65 Assault Crossing

In the Royal Army of Lunatavia the assault boats we use are, to say the least, rather clumsy!

In the war against the Colacocan forces (under General Pepsi) my company, 170 strong, had to cross the River Luna. Our assault boat, manned by a crew from our own company, had to make 20 trips to get us all across. After the last trip, the crew left the boat on the far side and joined the rest of the company.

On our left, Z Company had to make 30 trips to get all 240 of their men across in their assault boat.

How many are there in the crew of a Lunative assault boat, and how many passengers does it carry?

66 Letter Cubes

Here is a more difficult version of Problem 21, because there are only two cubes visible, not three.

These two identical cubes have the letters S, V, I, X, H and O arranged on the six sides. Can you say, from what you can see, which pairs of letters are on the opposite faces to each other?

67 Stepping Stones

The River Adder is 5 metres wide where three evenly-spaced stepping stones form a crossing place. Each stone is one metre square.

The River Viper is four times as wide, and is crossed by an exactly similar set of stepping stones. How many of these stones are there?

68 Port and Starboard

(*from an idea suggested by Dallas Paige*)

The other day I was in a helicopter above the long narrow channel leading to Boothport harbour. The fog was so thick that I was sure no ship would be visible from another one more than 20 metres away. By a freak effect, from above I could see that there were five ships all in a line in the channel, all moving slowly at the same speed. All I could really see were their lights – a *red light* on the port (left-hand) side, and a *green light* on the starboard (right-hand) side of each. Here's how it looked to me (for red, for green):

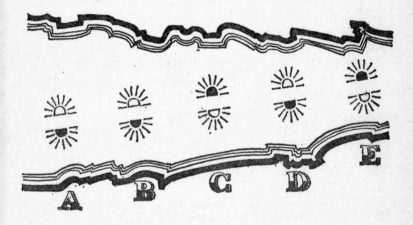

I realised that disaster was imminent, and, sure enough, the next minute two ships had collided.

Which two (out of A, B, C, D and E)?

69 Digital Sums

As you probably know, *all* numbers divisible by 3 have the sum (i.e., total) of their digits also divisible by 3, e.g., the number 741 is divisible by 3, and so is 7 + 4 + 1 (= 12). This useful fact also applies to numbers divisible by 9, but not in general to any others.

But can you find all the three-figure numbers which are divisible by 7, and which *do* have the sum of their digits divisible by 7? There are, in fact, 21 of them, including those beginning with 0, such as 007 (a Number Bond, perhaps?).

70 Relatively Speaking

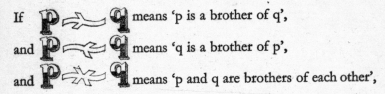

If   means 'p is a brother of q',

and   means 'q is a brother of p',

and   means 'p and q are brothers of each other',

then can you put in all the missing parts of this diagram?

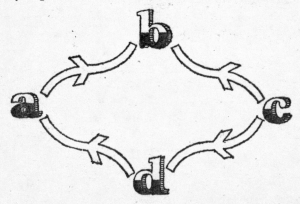

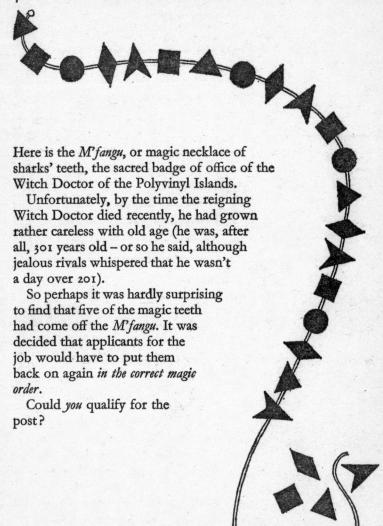

Here is the *M'fangu*, or magic necklace of sharks' teeth, the sacred badge of office of the Witch Doctor of the Polyvinyl Islands.

Unfortunately, by the time the reigning Witch Doctor died recently, he had grown rather careless with old age (he was, after all, 301 years old – or so he said, although jealous rivals whispered that he wasn't a day over 201).

So perhaps it was hardly surprising to find that five of the magic teeth had come off the *M'fangu*. It was decided that applicants for the job would have to put them back on again *in the correct magic order*.

Could *you* qualify for the post?

72 A-maze-ing

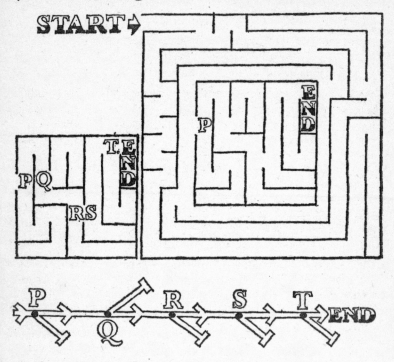

Mazes, however complicated, can be reduced to simpler diagrams which give enough information to guide you in and out (rather like a London Underground map).

As an example, the smaller maze on the left can be reduced to the lower diagram, which shows that the directions for entering are: LEFT, RIGHT, LEFT, LEFT, LEFT. (For coming out the directions would be: RIGHT, RIGHT, RIGHT, LEFT, RIGHT.) To help you to see what is happening, I have marked in letters at the points where there is a choice.

Can you make your own simplified diagram for the larger maze, which actually incorporates the smaller one as a central 'island'? (I have left the point P marked.)

73 Sum Mystery

$$\begin{array}{r} A\ B\ B\ B \\ -\quad A\ A\ A \\ \hline C\ C\ C\ A \end{array}$$

Here is a subtraction sum disguised with three letters A, B and C which stand (not necessarily in that order) for three *consecutive* single-figure numbers such as 1, 2 and 3.

Can you unravel the mystery, and so find what number the word CAB stands for?

74 When in Rome

(*a*) Which Roman numbers, each making use of two different numerals, read the same from left to right as they do from right to left? (There are three of them.)
(*b*) Which *one* of these numbers also looks exactly the same when turned upside down?

75 Whatever Next?

Can you say what the next number is in each of these sequences?

SEQUENCE A	2	5	8	11	14
SEQUENCE B	3	8	16	27	41
SEQUENCE C	4	12	28	55	96

76 Party Piece

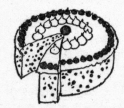

I was 'helping' my wife with the children's party.

'Do you think,' she asked, 'that without making *too* many mistakes, you could find out how many of our 25 guests want ice-cream, how many want jelly and how many want cake?'

'Nothing easier,' I replied confidently, 'it's a piece of cake.'

Dodging a well-aimed sausage roll, I went off and soon came back with the information.

'Fourteen want ice-cream, twelve want cake and ten want jelly. Also,' I went on, feeling rather proud of myself, 'of those wanting ice-cream, four want cake as well but no jelly, while two want jelly as well but no cake. Of course that fat Jones boy wants all three. There, how's that for attention to detail?'

'Not so good,' she replied, 'you've forgotten to find out how many want cake and jelly *without* ice-cream!'

'Well we can soon work that out,' I said quickly, 'let's see now, the number is, er . . .'

What?

77 Trellis Work

The bars of the triangular framework are marked in six different ways, and the different bars are arranged to a pattern.

What are the markings on the five bars at the bottom of the framework, lettered A, B, C, D and E?

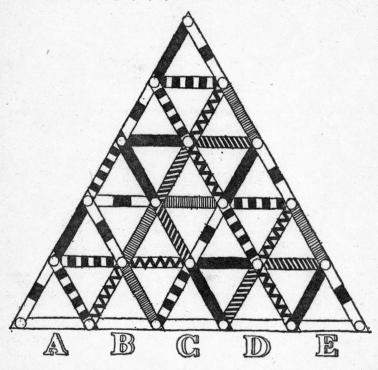

A   B   C   D   E

78 Where There's a Will...

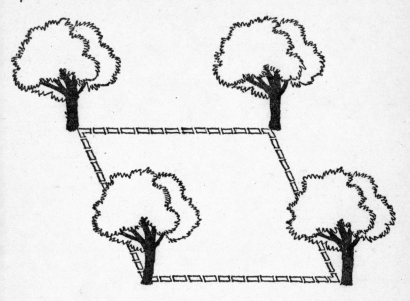

That eccentric nobleman, Sir Primely Booth, left in his will a bequest to the town to build an open-air swimming pool for public use, *provided* it was built so that his four famous Ten Metre Trees were each right next to the water in the pool.

Now, these trees stand one at each corner of a square of side 10 metres – hence the name. The town architect objected that the area occupied by the pool would be too small. However, an alternative plan was drawn up making *much* better use of the space – a plan which, no doubt, the noble benefactor had had in mind all the time!

(*a*) What is the *smallest* area a square pool could occupy?

(*b*) What is the *largest* area a square pool could occupy?

79 Hexagons

(six sides, each side equal in length to the one opposite)

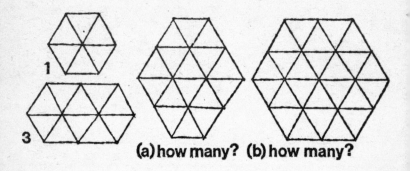

1

3

(a) how many? (b) how many?

80 A Challenge!

Add up all the whole numbers from 1 to 200 inclusive – go on, you have *one minute* to do so!

81 More Trees

Ten small trees are numbered from 1 to 10, and are planted in numerical order 10 metres apart from each other. How far is it from tree No 1 to tree No 10
  (a) if they are all arranged in a straight line?
  (b) if they are all arranged in a circle?

82 A Question of Speed

(*a*) I expect you've met this old chestnut before:

I need to travel at an average speed of 50 kilometres per hour if I am to arrive on time for my appointment 50 kilometres away; for the first half of the journey, traffic conditions are bad, and I only manage to average half the required speed; what speed must I average for the second half of the journey if I am to arrive on time?

(*b*) Got it? Well here's a similar sounding problem with a rather different answer:

Suppose this time I manage to achieve *twice* the required average speed for the first half of the journey; what speed must I then average for the second half in order to arrive exactly on time? What fraction is this of the required speed?

83 One More River to Cross

The famous Bailey–Jones Bridge is used for crossing rivers in many parts of the world. Its success is due to its strong but simple design – every span is exactly 50 metres long.

Here is a sketch of the bridge across the River Niffy; as you see, two piers are needed to support the spans:

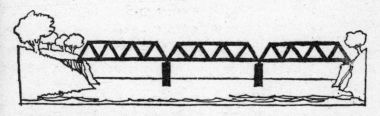

The River Whiffy is three times as wide. How many piers are needed for the bridge there?

84 In Rome Again

If a Roman citizen had been allowed to use one each of the numerals I, X, C and M

(a) what is the *largest* number he could have made with them?

(b) what is the *smallest* number he could have made with them?

85 Shop!

There is a row of five shops near my house, in the order shown above.

The five owners are Mrs Comb (who is not the Hairdresser), Mr Plum (who is not the Greengrocer), Mr Pill (who is not the Chemist), Mr Salt (who is not the Grocer) and Miss Rose (who is not the Florist).

Miss Rose owns one of the end shops in the row. Mr Pill has his shop next to the Grocer, and is always very friendly with the Greengrocer, who (he hopes) will sell him her shop one day.

Who owns which shop?

86 Magic Beads

Local legend tells of a magic amulet buried by Merlin on a hill-top in our neighbourhood. One historian quotes an old saying to the effect that:

FINDER OF MERLIN'S CHARM BENEATH
YOU'LL NE'ER BE TROUBLED WITH YOUR TEETH

although he unkindly suggests that perhaps all the finder's teeth may fall out.

Recently, digging in our hill-top garden, I found this circlet. As you can see, 12 black and white beads are still embedded in it, but four seem to be missing. I thought that, if I could guess what the missing beads looked like, I might be able to get hold of suitable replacements and fit them in. The matter is urgent, as my next visit to the dentist is due soon.

Can you help? I have labelled the four spaces A, B, C and D.

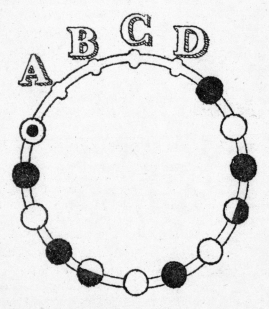

87 Mastermind

I expect you have played this excellent game. For those who are new to it, one player forms a line of four coloured pegs which are concealed from the other player, who tries to find out the colour 'code' used. To do this, he arranges a line of four pegs of his own, which is then 'marked' by the first player. The marking is done by up to four black or white markers. Each *black* marker means one peg is of correct colour and in the correct place. Each *white* marker means one peg is of correct colour but in the wrong place. Based on this information, the second player puts in another line, which is also marked, and so the game continues until the code is 'cracked'.

Here are four sample games with their marking. Can you say in each case what the correct line is? (The first one is very easy, the last one quite hard.)

GAME A RED – YELLOW – RED – YELLOW ○ ○ ○ ○

GAME B RED – BLUE – GREEN – YELLOW ○ ○ ○ ○
　　　　　 BLUE – RED – GREEN – YELLOW ● ● ○ ○

GAME C BLUE – BLUE – BLUE – BLUE ● ●
　　　　　 BLUE – BLUE – GREEN – GREEN ● ● ○
　　　　　 GREEN – BLUE – BLUE – YELLOW ● ● ○ ○

GAME D YELLOW – YELLOW – RED – RED ● ● ○
　　　　　 GREEN – GREEN – RED – RED ●
　　　　　 BLUE – BLUE – BLUE – BLUE ●
　　　　　 YELLOW – GREEN – RED – GREEN ○ ○

88 Mad Metro

You've heard enough about Lunatavia by now to expect that the underground railway system of Lunaville, the capital city, would not run in a normal sort of way. Nor would you be disappointed! Here it is, all 13 stations of it:

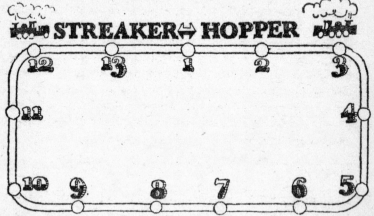

The Hopper and The Streaker are the local names for the two trains which run on the system. The Hopper hops from Station No 1 to No 4, to No 7, and so on, returning to No 1 after three circuits. The Streaker – naturally – goes the other way! It streaks from Station No 1 to No 10, to No 6, and so on, returning to No 1 after four circuits. A really Lunative system!

The cost of a ticket is 1 Luna for each journey from one stop to the next (e.g., from No 10 to No 6 on the Streaker). We used to have fun when I was a student at the famous Luna Bin (that's their equivalent of our Polytechnic). We would work out the *cheapest* way of getting to and fro.

For instance, my daily journey from Station No 4 to No 8 would have cost 10 Lunas by Hopper or 12 Lunas by Streaker. So instead, I went by Hopper to Station No 7, then changed and completed the journey by Streaker – total cost only 4 Lunas.

Try your hand at working out the cheapest way of getting from Station No 10 to No 12, and then getting back again afterwards.

89 Magic Square

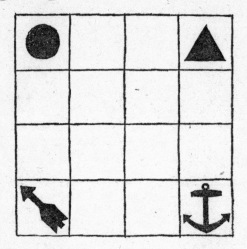

Can you complete this 'Magic Square', so that each of the four rows across, each of the four columns up and down, and each of the two diagonals from corner to corner contains one each of the four signs – Triangle, Circle, Arrow and Anchor?

There are two possible solutions (but perhaps you can find more?).

90 Sock Burglar

Yes! he's struck again – taking socks out of a drawer in the dark (no torch?). In the drawer are six identical green socks mixed with two identical blue socks. Assuming our burglar knows this in advance, what is the *smallest* number of socks he must remove to be sure of finding when he gets home that he has

(*a*) a pair of *green* socks?
(*b*) a pair of *blue* socks?
(*c*) a pair of socks (green *or* blue, but not mixed)?

91 Donkey Derby

(from an idea suggested by Peter Tokely)

As the eight donkeys ambled, walked or were dragged past the finishing post at our local fete, a keen observer would have noticed that:

(*a*) Eeyore was a nose in front of The Moke

(*b*) Carrots was three places behind Brownie

(*c*) Daisy's rider could see five donkeys in front of her

(*d*) Brownie was between Big-Ears and Clover

(*e*) Clementine was three places in front of Eeyore

(*f*) naughty Big-Ears was nibbling the tail of the donkey ahead of him.

Who was first? Who was last?

92 Still More Triangles
(from an idea suggested by Michael Tuckwell)

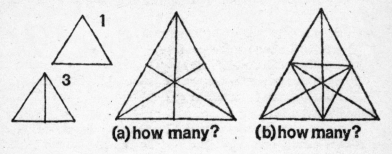

(a) how many?   **(b) how many?**

93 Mixed Bag
(from an idea suggested by Neil Pockett)

Boothbars cost 6p each, Boothchews are 1p each, while Booth-drops are literally 10 a penny. If I spend exactly 70p and buy exactly 70 sweets altogether, how many of each sort do I get? (Assume I have *some* of each sort.)

94 Birthday Puzzle

The combined age of John and his younger brother James is twice the difference between their ages.

When their combined age becomes three times the difference James will be 10.

How old are they each now?

95 Clockwise?

If I told you that a friend of mine had actually seen a clock in which

  (*a*) there is only one hand (the hour hand)
  (*b*) this hand travels *counter*-clockwise
  (*c*) the dial is marked with 24 hours
  (*d*) the dial numbering starts at the bottom instead of the top
  (*e*) this clock was made in the 15th century

would you believe me?

If you've ever been to Florence (in Italy, *not* Lunatavia) you probably would, because it stands in the Cathedral there. It is a most beautiful clock, associated with the name of a famous artist, Ucello, and this sketch doesn't look much like it:

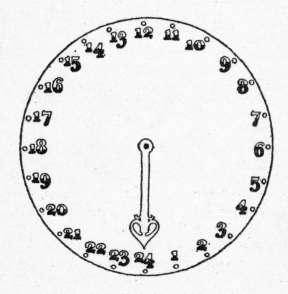

Now the problem is this: assuming this clock keeps perfect time, when will its hand coincide with (be in the same place on the dial as) the hourhand of a normal 12-hour clock?

96 Repeater

On a much smaller scale than the Cathedral Clock of Florence, the gold watch my father gave me is the type which used to be called a 'Repeater'. If you press a little catch, the chimes tell you the time *to the nearest minute*! It works like this:

(a) one stroke for every hour past
(b) a double stroke (on another note) for every quarter past the hour
(c) further strokes (on yet another note) for the number of minutes past the quarter hour.

For example, at 6.35 it strikes 6 strokes (six o'clock) plus 4 strokes (two quarters past six) plus 5 strokes (five minutes past the half-hour), a total of 15 strokes.

Perhaps you would like to work out at what other times between 6 and 7 o'clock this delightful watch will strike 15 times.

97 Puppies

Here are some statements about puppies. Of course, you may not agree with all of them. But just suppose they *were* all correct, what conclusion could you draw from them?

(a) No puppy that chases cats is unteachable.
(b) No puppy without a black nose will play with a kangaroo.
(c) Puppies with floppy ears always chase cats.
(d) No teachable puppy has a loud bark.
(e) No puppies have black noses unless they have floppy ears.

98 Yacht Race

Here is a sketch of the triangular course for our annual 'Three-buoys Race'. The Commodore of our Yacht Club is an old Square-rigged Sailor, as he often tells us, and doesn't 'hold with these modern compass bearings; the old Mariner's Compass got us round the Horn' – that's why the course for the first leg of the race is given as East-North-East.

What are the courses (by the Mariner's Compass, naturally) for the other two legs of the race?

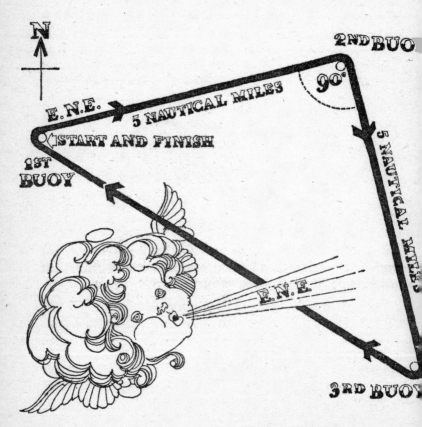

99 How's That Again?

He said 'What was that that you said I said she said?' he said.
  I said 'Who said you said she said?' I said.
  He said 'You said I said she said,' he said.
  I said 'I said you said she said I said "What?" ' I said.
What *did* she say?

100 Calling the Cows Home

My farmer friend has an odd way of naming his eight cows.
  'I called them by numbers at first,' he said, 'they always establish their own order of precedence, you know. But my wife wanted names instead, so we compromised. Ann is the leader, and that's Jo following her. There's my own favourite,' he went on pointing to the sixth in line, 'she's Jo-Win, but my wife prefers the last one there, Jo-Jo.'
  One of the cows was soon to have a calf. Her name was Ann-Win, I was told.
  'Won't you run into difficulties when you come to name the calf, using your system?' I asked.
  'Yes, I shall have to give her a *triple* name,' said my friend, 'I expect you can guess what it will be, can't you?'
  Can you?

1 Triangles

(*a*) 13 and (*b*) 27 triangles.

Made up as follows:

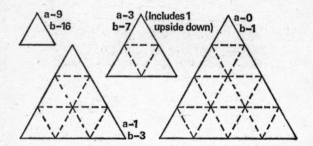

a–9
b–16

a–3
b–7

(Includes 1
upside down)

a–0
b–1

a–1
b–3

2 A Striking Problem

1.30 AM

This 'striking' result only occurs once during each 12-hour period, when the clock strikes for 12.30, 1 o'clock and 1.30. As it was still dark, the time was 1.30 AM, not PM.

3 Noughts and Crosses

(*a*) Square 5. (*b*) Square 4.

In each case you will then have two choices for your winning row.

4 Collision Course

(*a*) Z. (*b*) (i) W. (ii) U. (*c*) They will already have collided at Y.

Here are the courses of the two engines in each case:

(*a*) BLACK: A U Y B Z T A U Y B Z T A U Y B Z
    WHITE: Z S T U V W X Y Z S T U V W X Y Z

(*b*) (i) BLACK: A U Y
      WHITE: W X Y

  (ii) BLACK: A U Y B Z T A U Y B Z T A U Y B Z T A U Y
      WHITE: U V W X Y Z S T U V W X Y Z S T U V W X Y

(*c*) BLACK: . . . . . Y (B Z T)
    WHITE: . . . . . Y (Z S T)

5 Coloured Numbers

It is red.

An ODD number added to an EVEN number gives an ODD result, hence the colour! (Even you must admit it's odd – Sorry!)

6 Suicide Squad

He should stand at T.

On the first 'round' of this macabre game, R shoots S, T shoots U, V shoots W, X shoots Y and Z shoots R. On the second round, T shoots V and X shoots Z. Finally, T shoots X.

7 Number Wheels

A – 1. B – 5 or 15. C – $\frac{4}{7}$. D – 11. E – 9. F – 14.

A Double each time. B Odd numbers. C Add 1 to the top, 2 to the bottom each time. D Add 1, then 2, then 3, then 4. E 1 × 1, 2 × 2, 3 × 3, ... ('Square' numbers). F Add 3 each time.

8 The Sultan's Choice

If I had worn a black disc, my opponent would have known his was white, because there is only one black disc. As he made no move, I knew mine must be white.

9 Which Numbers?

Possible sets of numbers:

TRIANGLE	2	3	4	6
SQUARE	4 or 1	9 or 1	8 or 2	9 or 4
CIRCLE	1 or 4	1 or 9	2 or 8	4 or 9

So, for example, the tablet could read: 3 × 3 = 9 × 1

10 Compass Square

Mr East lives on the *west* side.

Mr North cannot live on the north side (his own name) nor the west side (not further west than Mr West) nor the east side (Mr South lives further east) so it's the *south* side for him. This gives *east* for Mr South and *north* for Mr West (who can't live on the west side), leaving only the *west* side for Mr East.

11 Sum Code

INNS stands for 5117.

N must be 1 ('carry' figure from S + S). So I is 5, to give I + I + 1 carried = 11 (remember 0 is not one of the figures allowed). So S = 7 to give S + S + 1 carried = 15. (We don't need to know X or E; we know that X + X gives a carry figure, so values of X and E could be 6 and 2 or 8 and 6 or 9 and 8, e.g., the sum could be 756 + 756 = 1512.)

12 On the Buses

At 11.12½ AM

Bill (10 minutes ahead of Arthur) will reach the Pier at 11.5. After 5 minutes he will start back, at 11.10. Arthur is then 5 minutes away from the Pier. So they should meet half-way, that is 2½ minutes later, at 11.12½.

13 Join the Points

66 lines.

Each of the 12 points is joined to 11 others. 12 × 11 = 132. Since each line has been counted twice, this figure must be halved.

14 A Bowling Problem

Move the bowls with your right hand as follows:

(1) Bowl 1 from cupboard into bowl 2 in left hand.
(2) Bowls 1 and 2 from left hand into bowl 3 in cupboard.
(3) Bowls 1, 2 and 3 from cupboard into bowl 4 in left hand.
(4) All four bowls into bowl 5 in cupboard.

This is one of several possible solutions.

15 Squares

(*a*) 22 and (*b*) 46 squares.
Made up as follows:

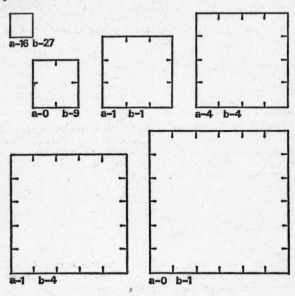

a–16 b–27

a–0   b–9   a–1   b–1   a–4   b–4

a–1   b–4   a–0   b–1

16 Double Bullseye

X=6, Y=1.
X and Y start off each repeating sequence of numbers connected to them,
such as:

6 – 8 4 2 6 8 (4 2 6 8 4 2 6 ....)
1 – 7 9 3 1 7 (9 3 1 7 9 3 1 ....)

These sequences turn up as the right-hand (or 'unit') figure when the inner
figure is a repeated multiplier, e.g., 7; 7 × 7=49; 9 × 7=63; 3 × 7=21;
1 × 7=7 ....

17 Racing News

First Bill, second Colin, third Alan.

Alan's and Bill's statements about Alan disagree, so one of them is the liar. Colin disagrees with Alan, so Alan must have lied. So Colin was second (said Bill), beating Alan (said Colin) who was therefore last. So Bill (not second, said Colin) must be the winner. As a check, these results disagree with Alan's statements.

18 Target

74 points.

Proceed by the path 3 – 8 – 12 – 16 – 17 – 18 – TARGET.

19 League Table

Lost to Puncham, drew with Kickham, beat Foulham.

Puncham had 5 points out of 6, so won two matches and drew once – with Kickham (the only team not beaten by Puncham).

Tripham's 3 points must come from a win (2), a draw (1), and the loss to Puncham.

So the two teams who never won a match were Kickham and Foulham. Therefore all Kickham's 3 points came from draws, which would account for Foulham's only point.

Tripham, then, drew with Kickham and beat Foulham.

20 Drink Problem

The empty bottle costs 2½p.

NO! not 5p, because then the drink itself would cost 20p (total 25p), only 15p more than the empty bottle.

21 Brick-work

The all-black face is opposite the circle, the square opposite the star, and the cross opposite the dot.

The all-black face appears on two bricks, from which it is obviously *not* opposite the cross, star, square or dot; so it *must* be opposite the circle.

By the same method the square (which appears twice) *must* be opposite the star, while the cross (also appearing twice) *must* be opposite the dot.

22 Pentagon

(*a*) Go in at B (or D). (*b*) Come out at D (or B). (*c*) 3 hours, 10 minutes.

If I go in at any point except B or D, I shall have to traverse at least one corridor more than once, adding a certain amount extra on to my time of 190 minutes for the 19 corridors.

What's so special about B and D? They are the only rooms which have an *odd* number of corridors leaving them.

23 Round Trip

Going – faster by 10 minutes; returning – slower by 10 minutes.

Here are both systems set out stop by stop for comparison:

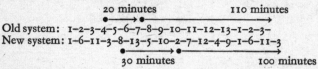

```
                20 minutes                  110 minutes
Old system:  1-2-3-4-5-6-7-8-9-10-11-12-13-1-2-3-
New system:  1-6-11-3-8-13-5-10-2-7-12-4-9-1-6-11-3
                30 minutes              100 minutes
```

24 Watch Out!

Yes, at 3 o'clock.

The markings are for 15 minutes and for 15 o'clock.

25 Rectangles

(*a*) 15 and (*b*) 35 rectangles.
Made up as follows:

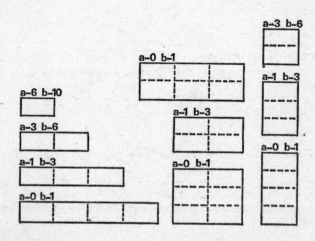

26 Waxwork

1 metre tall.

This is exactly half the original height, because if width, depth and height are all reduced to half the original, then the new volume will be reduced to one-eighth ($\frac{1}{2} \times \frac{1}{2} \times \frac{1}{2} = \frac{1}{8}$). So eight models each half-size can be made.

27 Guess the Pattern

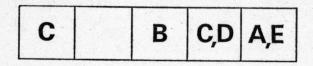

Counting from the left of each line, A occurs every 6 spaces, B every 7, C every 3, D every 4 and E every 5.

28 Tangled Ages

Tim's age is either 14 or 15 or 17.

George (3 years off John's age) is either 13 or 19, so Bill (1 year younger) is either 12 or 18. That allows Tim's age (between Bill's and John's) the three possibilities shown.

29 What Shape?

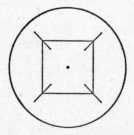

Each figure in the bottom row is found by combining the figures in the two rows above it.

30 Cut the Cards

11 cards.

The diagram shows how this is done. Only a small strip one centimetre wide by 60 centimetres long is wasted – not enough for another card.

31 Money Mad

31 Lunas.

All amounts above this can be made up using coins. Here are some examples:

$32 - 9, 9, 9, 5$; $33 - 9, 9, 5, 5, 5$; $36 - 9, 9, 9, 9$; $37 - 9, 9, 9, 5, 5$.

Note for the interested: $31 = (9 \times 5) - (9 + 5)$

32 Topo-bricks

7 different shapes, but only 5 if each face is white.

Here they are:

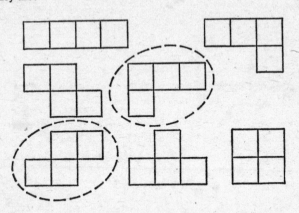

33 Weird Numbers

$3 + 4 = 2;$ $3 \times 4 = 2;$ $3 - 4 = 4!!!$

Since 6 is written 1, 5 is presumably written 0. So 10 (twice 5) is also written 0 as stated in the problem, and so is 20 (twice 10), which would fit in with 23 being written 3.

This repetition of numbering shows that it is a 'clock-face' system as shown, with 0 appearing after 4. So 7 (i.e., 3 + 4) and 12 (i.e., 3 × 4) both appear as 2.

To find (3 − 4), start at 3 and count back 4 places, giving the answer 4 which looks so strange.

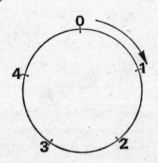

34 The Truth Game

(*a*) Z must be true. (*b*) X might be true. (*c*) Y cannot be true.

Z must be true because 'some of my aunts drink cider' and none of them is a donkey.

X might be true because 'all donkeys have long ears', but so presumably do some other creatures – possibly including my aunts.

Y cannot be true because 'none of my aunts is a donkey'.

35 More Triangles

(*a*) 24 and (*b*) 44 triangles.

Each 'layer' splits up into the 10 triangles shown below on the left. There are two of these layers in the first diagram (20 triangles) and four in the second (40 triangles).

There are also in each diagram four extra triangles as shown below on the right, making up the totals given.

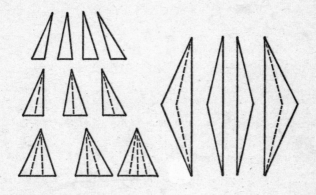

36 Handy Angles

(*a*) On top at 7·38. (*b*) At right angles at 7·22 *and* 7·55. (*c*) Opposite at 7·05.

The minute hand (MH) gains on the hour hand (HH) all the time. This gain can be measured as 55 'minute-spaces' in every 60 minutes of time, or 1 minute-space in every $1\frac{1}{11}$ minutes.

At 7 o'clock HH stands 35 minute-spaces ahead of MH.

When MH catches up 5 spaces it is in opposition to HH; 20 spaces, at right angles; 35 spaces, on top; 50 spaces, at right angles again.

These intervals take exactly $5\frac{5}{11}$, $21\frac{9}{11}$, $38\frac{2}{11}$ and $54\frac{6}{11}$ minutes to catch up.

37 Rolling Dice

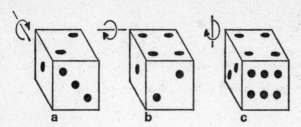

38 Dice Again

The ? face is marked 3.

The touching faces must be 2 (opposite 5). The left-hand die can be put in the other die's position as follows: roll a quarter turn away from you to bring 1 on the bottom face to the front and 4 to the top; then roll half a turn sideways, so interchanging left and right faces, and also top and bottom faces. So the top face will be the opposite to 4, that is 3.

39 Odd and Even

The first number was EVEN.

Since the answer obtained by adding the two results together was odd, one result must have been odd and one even.

But only if an odd number is multiplied by another odd number will the result be odd. So the second number (multiplied by an odd number) must be odd, giving an even first number.

40 Black and White Cars

7 black cars, 5 white cars.

The 34-cm box must contain 5 black and 2 white cars (20 cm and 14 cm).

The 29-cm box must contain 2 black and 3 white cars (8 cm and 21 cm).

41 A Look into the Future

Sunday, 1st January, 2062.   Monday, 1st January, 2057.

These rather strange results (the Sunday gap is 11 years, the Monday one 5 years) are due to the effect of leap years.

Each year January 1st is normally one day later in the week (365 days= 52 weeks + 1 day). But 2052, 2056 and 2060 are leap years (divisible by 4). The extra day delays the following January 1st by a further day in the week.

Here are the weekdays for 1st January each year: 2051 Sunday. 2052 Monday. 2053 Wednesday. 2054 Thursday. 2055 Friday. 2056 Saturday. 2057 *Monday*. 2058 Tuesday. 2059 Wednesday. 2060 Thursday. 2061 Saturday. 2062 *Sunday*.

42 Breakfast Menu

4 Children.

The total of the numbers shown is 29, which is 8 more than are in the form.

Those who like all three items will appear in each of the numbers shown for porridge and bacon, for bacon and eggs, and for eggs and porridge.

So the same children will appear three times in the total, i.e. two times too many.

Therefore the extra 8 in the total is twice the number who like all three items, that is twice 4.

43 Parallelograms

(a) 18 and (b) 35 parallelograms.

Made up as follows:

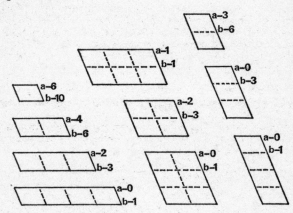

44 Cyclo-cross

A – B – C – E – G. Equivalent to 18 kilometres by road.

From A to C the road route (4 kilometres) is shorter than the cross-country route (equivalent to 5 kilometres by road).

From C to G there are four routes. Here they are with their equivalent distances by road in kilometres.

C – E – F – G: $4 + 6 + 5 = 15$
C – G: $3 \times 5 = 15$
C – D – G: $(2\frac{1}{2} \times 5) + 2 = 14\frac{1}{2}$
C – E – G: $4 + (2 \times 5) = 14$ which is the shortest.

So the total equivalent distance by road in kilometres for the best route is $4 + 14 = 18$.

45 A Tartan Problem

The answer can be found quite easily by following the diagonal patterns of the squares occupied by any particular shading.

For a more systemic method you must turn to the Mad Major's 'secret formula'! If you think of the squares as being numbered from 1 to 100 you will find that each type of shading recurs after the same interval:

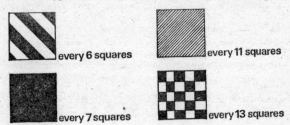

46 Bomb Scare

Never!

Here is the sequence of events:

Time	Lamp 1	Lamp 2
9.0 AM	GREEN	GREEN
9.1	Automatic change to RED	
9.2	Automatic change to GREEN	

BOTH LAMPS ARE NOW GREEN – – – – BUT –

10 seconds later		Change to RED due to red-green change in Lamp 1
9.3	Automatic change to RED	
9.4	Automatic change to GREEN	
10 seconds later		Change to GREEN due to red-green change in Lamp 1

BOTH LAMPS ARE NOW GREEN – – – – BUT –

10 seconds later	Change to RED due to red-green change in Lamp 2	
9.5	Automatic change to GREEN	

BOTH LAMPS ARE NOW GREEN – – – – BUT –

10 seconds later		Change to RED due to red-green change in Lamp 1

This process is repeated indefinitely, the two lamps *never* staying on green together for the 30 seconds needed to explode the bomb.

47 Seating Problem

All of them!

Since 8 adults *or* 12 children can be seated, presumably 3 children occupy the seats of 2 adults. So if I ask 4 children to stand (as permitted by the regulations) there will then be 6 adults and 3 children occupying the seats for 8 adults.

48 The Dancing Men

DOGS GOOD   GOOSE OFF FOOD

As with Sherlock Holmes' famous case, each figure stands presumably for a letter. The clue is the word DOGS which surely must be part of the message. There are three words with the right number of letters, but two of them will not do – they each contain a double letter.

So we now have:

DOGS

The message still contains two unknown figures, but it now reads:

DOGS GOOD GOOS ⊤ O ⋀⋀ ⋀OOD,

and very little trial and error is needed to find out that ⊤ must be E and ⋀ must be F.

49 Kitchen Tiles

Tiles covered by Father 47, by Mother 76.
Here are their two solutions:

Father

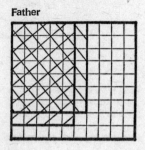

Mother

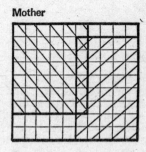

50 Tri-dominoes

7 different shapes.
Here they are:

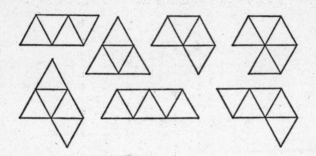

51 Murder!

D was the murderer.

Each man gave one 'did' and one 'did not'.

If the 'did' is true, then so must the 'did not' be true. But this is impossible, one of the two statements must be false in each case. Therefore each 'did' statement is false, and each 'did not' true.

This rules out A, B and C, leaving D as the murderer.

52 International Date Line

1 AM on Sunday 15th.

Since the sun rises in the east, local time just to the *west* of the Date Line is 12 hours AHEAD of Greenwich, while local time just to the *east* of the Date Line is 12 hours BEHIND Greenwich – a whole day's difference between the two positions.

So by crossing the Date Line from east to west that day is 'lost'. That is why the answer is *not* 1 AM on Saturday 14th.

53 Cipher Message

GOLDFINGER KILLED

Here is the grid filled in ready for enciphering or deciphering. You can make up your own private code by using a different code phrase.

	1	2	3	4	5
1	B	R	A	I/J	N
2	T	C	K	L	E
3	S	D	F	G	H
4	M	O	P	Q	U
5	V	W	X	Y	Z

54 Nim

Remove two counters from the centre pile of five.

Then, whatever move your opponent makes, you will be in a position to reduce the game to two equal piles. This leads eventually to him removing one pile, leaving you to win by removing the last remaining pile.

55 Circular Pattern

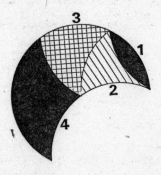

Each of the 1 and 2 shapes have the same repeating pattern of three different shadings.

Each of the 3 and 4 shapes have differing repeating patterns of two different shadings.

56 Sweet Tooth

It will cost 11p.

In the last two weeks I have spent a total of 44p on four packets of each sort of sweet. So one packet of each sort must cost one quarter of 44p, that is 11p.

57 More Mad Money

(*a*) 2 Squares and 2 Circles.
(*b*) 1 Pentagon, 2 Triangles and 3 Circles.
(*c*) 45 Lunas.

Since each coin is worth four of the next smaller coin, their actual value in Lunas must be as shown in the table below. Using this table, even the most Lunative money problems can be solved!

1 Circle	=	1 Luna
1 Triangle	=	4 Lunas
1 Square	=	16 Lunas
1 Pentagon	=	64 Lunas

58 Trapeziums

(*a*) 12 and (*b*) 30 trapeziums.

Made up as follows:

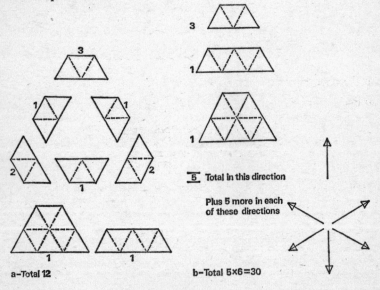

a–Total 12

b–Total 5×6=30

59 Age Differences

(*a*) NO. (*b*) YES. (*c*) YES. (*d*) 5 years.

There are 8 possible arrangements of the ages:

1 A – B – C – D

5 A – $\frac{B}{D}$ – C

2 D – C – B – A

6 C – $\frac{B}{D}$ – A

3 $\begin{array}{c} A - B \\ C - D \end{array}$

7 B – $\frac{A}{C}$ – D

4 $\begin{array}{c} B - A \\ D - C \end{array}$

8 D – $\frac{A}{C}$ – B

None of these arrangements fits (*a*).
Arrangement No 8 fits (*b*).
Arrangements Nos 5, 6, 7 and 8 fit (*c*).
Arrangements Nos 3 and 4 fit (*d*).

60 Jig-saws

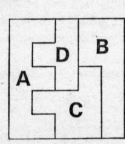
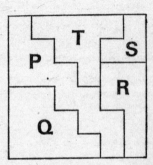

61 Target Practice

10 bulls.

Made up as follows:
Green: last 3 shots must all be bulls to make up 35.
Brown: last 4 shots totalled 31. 5, 5, 5, 16 or 7, 7, 7, 10 or 9, 9, 9, 4. *No* 16 or 4, so last shot was a bull, like his first one.
White: 6, 6, 8, 8, 13 or 6, 6, 10, 10, 9 or 8, 8, 10, 10, 5. *No* 13, so he scored 2 bulls.
Black: scored 39 with his first 4 shots, so one was 9, the other 3 bulls.

62 One to Twenty

Start with 2, then go on to 5, 8, 11, 14, 17, 20.

If you add 3 more each time to your previous call, your opponent cannot affect the situation, as he can only add 1 or 2 each time; e.g., after you start with 2, he can say 3 or 4; either way you can still say 5.

63 Another Bomb Scare

The bomb blew up after *one* minute, not three!

As the diagram clearly shows, the *start* of Vol I is next to Vol II, which in turn is next to the *end* of Vol III. So the fuse actually only ran through the 1,000 pages of Vol II, taking 1 minute.

64 Regional Points

(*a*) 16 and (*b*) 31 regions.

I know it does seem that the series should run 1, 2, 4, 8, 16, 32, but it doesn't do that – hence the warning!

65 Assault Crossing

30 crew and 7 passengers!

Z Company needed 10 extra trips to carry 70 extra men, so there were 7 passengers each time. At 30 trips this totals 210 passengers, leaving 30 more men in Z Company – the crew.

As a check, my own company took 20 trips, giving 140 passengers and 30 crew, total 170.

Yes, the ratio of crew to passengers shows that we weren't too efficient in the Lunative army! Did I tell you our forces had to surrender after being bottled up by General Pepsi?

66 Letter Cubes

V opposite O, I opposite X, S opposite H.

All the letters appear next to O except for V. So V and O are opposites.

Roll the top cube a quarter turn towards you, giving O in front, X underneath, H at the side, X's opposite on top.

Now roll again a quarter turn to the left so that O stays in front, H is now underneath, X's opposite is on the left, H's opposite is on top. This is the final position of the cube, pairing together I and X, S and H.

67 Stepping Stones

13 stones.

Across the River Adder, the 3 stones take up 3 metres, and the 4 spaces take up the remaining 2 metres, making each space half a metre wide. So 1 stone + 1 space takes $1\frac{1}{2}$ metres, and there will always be one extra space taking up $\frac{1}{2}$ metre.

The River Viper is 20 metres wide (5×4); allow $\frac{1}{2}$ metre for the extra space, giving $19\frac{1}{2}$ metres to be bridged by 13 stones and gaps ($13 \times 1\frac{1}{2} = 19\frac{1}{2}$).

68 Port and Starboard

C and D collided.

There are only two ships headed directly for each other. Since red means left and green right, the directions of travel of the five ships – all moving at the same speed, remember – are as follows:

A   B   C   D   E

(No, don't ask me how they all got into their positions in the first place!)

69 Digital Sums

007, 070, 077, 133, 266, 322, 329, 392, 399, 455, 511, 518, 581, 588, 644, 700, 707, 770, 777, 833, 966.

How many did you get? I reckon a score of 14 or more ought to be rated GOOD.

70 Relatively Speaking

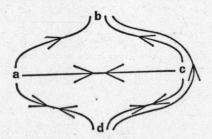

Since a and c are brothers of b, and c is a brother of d who is a brother of a, then a, c and d are all brothers of each other, and each is a brother of b.

And what about b? Well *he* might be the brother of a, c and d, or *she* might be their sister!

71 Witch Doctor's Test

In every 5 teeth the square, circle, diamond and arrowhead occur in the same order, but the triangle takes a different position each time, moving from left to right.

72 A-maze-ing

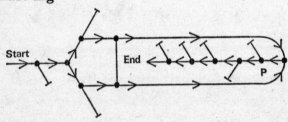

Here is a suggested layout. The 'doubling back' effect of the central 'island' is put in to agree with the direction of turn, depending from which direction P is approached.

73 Sum Mystery

CAB stands for 786.

In both the right-hand column and the one next to it, A is subtracted from B, but the answers are different. This must mean that A is larger than B, and the right-hand column really means B + 10 − A=A, or put another way, B + 10=2A.

Remembering that the difference between A and B can only be 1 or 2, trial shows that the only pairs of values which fit are: A=9, B=8 or A=8, B=6. In each case C must be 7, to give 3 consecutive numbers.

Only the second set gives a correct sum which is:

$$
\begin{array}{r}
8\ 6\ 6\ 6 \\
-\ \ \ 8\ 8\ 8 \\
\hline
7\ 7\ 7\ 8 \\
\end{array}
$$

74 When in Rome

(a) XIX   CXC   MCM.   (b) XIX.

These numbers stand for 19, for 190 and for 1900 respectively.

75 Whatever Next?

A – 17. B – 58. C – 154.

A is easy, just 3 more each time.

But A provides the answer to B, because the numbers in A are the *differences* between the numbers in B, e.g., $16 + 11 = 27$, $27 + 14 = 41$; so the next number is $41 + 17 = 58$.

In the same way the numbers in B are the differences between the numbers in C, e.g., $28 + 27 = 55$, $55 + 41 = 96$; so $96 + 58 = 154$.

76 Party Piece

3 children.

The total for the three groups – ice-cream, cake and jelly – comes to 36 $(14 + 12 + 10)$.

But this total includes one who wants all three items, and so has been counted *three times*. So the total must be reduced to 34 $(36 - 2)$.

However, this new total – which is 9 more than the correct figure of 25 – includes those who want two items each, and so have been counted *twice*. We know of 6 children $(4 + 2)$ who want two items, so the remaining 3 must be those who want cake and jelly, but not ice-cream.

77 Trellis Work

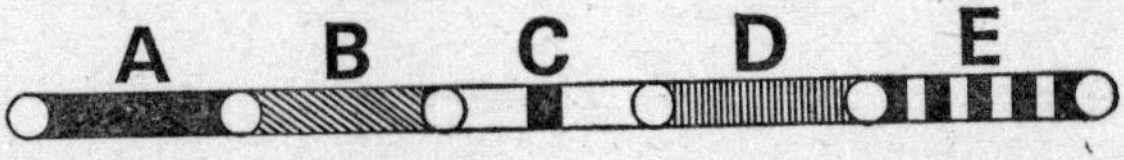

There are several patterns which could be followed to find the answers, but this is how the trellis work was actually constructed:

The triangles down the left-hand side of the frame have the same three shadings, but as they descend each time they rotate one-third of a turn *anti-clockwise*.

The next diagonal column of (upright) triangles have another set of three shadings, but this time as they descend each time they rotate one-third of a turn *clockwise*.

Successive diagonal columns of triangles repeat these patterns.

78 Where There's a Will …

(*a*) 100 and (*b*) 200 square metres.

The diagrams show how each answer is arrived at, the dotted lines helping to explain why one area is twice the other.

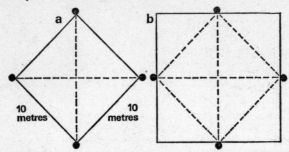

79 Hexagons

(*a*) 10 and (*b*) 29 hexagons.

Made up as follows:

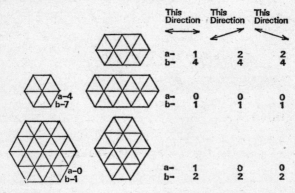

	This Direction ➡	This Direction ⬋	This Direction ➘
a–	1	2	2
b–	4	4	4
a–	0	0	0
b–	1	1	1
a–	1	0	0
b–	2	2	2

80 A Challenge!

20100.

There are *200 numbers* to be added altogether.

Because the interval between each is the same (they increase by 1), the *average* will lie half-way between the first and last numbers, i.e., $\frac{1}{2}(1 + 200)$ or 201/2.

So the total is *200 times* this average, that is:

$$200 \times \frac{201}{2} \text{ or } \frac{200}{2} \times 201 \text{ or } 100 \times 201, \text{ giving } 20100.$$

81 More Trees

(a) 90 and (b) 10 metres.

(a) The answer is *not* 100 metres – there are only 9 gaps. (b) The first and last trees stand next to each other in the circle!

82 A Question of Speed

(a) The speed of light!
(b) 33⅓ kilometres per hour, which is ⅔ of the average speed required.

(a) You have used up the whole of the hour you were allowed in travelling the first half of the journey. So you cannot arrive on time whatever you do.

(b) This time you take a quarter of an hour to travel 25 kilometres at a speed of 100 kilometres per hour (kph). So you have three-quarters of an hour for the remaining 25 kilometres, giving a speed of $(\frac{4}{3} \times 25)$ kph, or 33⅓ kph.

83 One More River to Cross

8 piers.

Because there are 9 spans needed for the bridge.

84 In Rome Again

(a) M C X I.   (b) C M I X.

(a) This stands for the number 1111. (b) This stands for the number 909.

85 Shop!

Hairdresser	Greengrocer	Chemist	Grocer	Florist
MISS ROSE	**MRS COMB**	**MR SALT**	**MR PLUM**	**MR PILL**

Miss Rose (*not* the Florist, but owns an end shop) must be the Hairdresser.
The Greengrocer (Mr Pill hopes to buy *her* shop) must be Mrs Comb.
Mr Pill (*not* the Chemist, but next to the Grocer) must be the Florist.
Mr Salt (*not* the Grocer) must be the Chemist.
Mr Plum can only be the Grocer.

86 Magic Beads

A   B   C   D

The pattern of beads in fours is: black – white – black – black and white, followed each time by: white – black – white – black and white.

87 Mastermind

GAME A YELLOW – RED – YELLOW – RED

The marking shows the correct colours are there, but *all* wrongly placed! As only two colours are used, there is only the one possible answer.

GAME B BLUE – RED – YELLOW – GREEN

Again, the first marking shows all correct colours but wrongly placed. The second marking shows that the Blue – Red switch has put two colours into their right places. It just remains to switch the other two colours.

GAME C YELLOW – BLUE – BLUE – GREEN

The first marking shows there are two Blues.
 The second marking shows there is also one Green, and that it and one of the Blues are correctly placed. There are four possibilities:

> BLUE – ? – GREEN – BLUE
> BLUE – ? – BLUE – GREEN
> ? – BLUE – GREEN – BLUE
> ? – BLUE – BLUE – GREEN

 The third marking shows the missing colour to be Yellow, and that the last of the four combinations is the only one which fits.

GAME D BLUE – YELLOW – YELLOW – RED

The first and second markings show two Yellows, only one Red and no Greens. Also that the Red must occupy one of the two right-hand spaces, the other one being Yellow. So there are four possibilities:

> YELLOW – ? – RED – YELLOW
> YELLOW – ? – YELLOW – RED
> ? – YELLOW – RED – YELLOW
> ? – YELLOW – YELLOW – RED

 The third marking shows the missing colour to be Blue.
 The fourth marking fits only the last of the four combinations.
 (Note the use of Green as a blank place-holder in the fourth line.)

88 Mad Metro

The total cost would be 7 Lunas (3 Lunas going, 4 Lunas returning).

Here is a comparative table, showing how the trains run:

HOPPER

$$1 - 4 - 7 - 10 - 13 - 3 - 6 - 9 - 12 - 2 - 5 - 8 - 11 - 1$$

STREAKER

$$1 - 10 - 6 - 2 - 11 - 7 - 3 - 12 - 8 - 4 - 13 - 9 - 5 - 1$$

Here is the journey going:

HOPPER	10 – 13 – 3	*or*	6 – 9 – 12
STREAKER	3 – 12		10 – 6

Here is the return journey:

HOPPER	12 – 2 – 5	*or*	4 – 7 – 10
STREAKER	5 – 1 – 10		12 – 8 – 4

You are invited to discover cheaper ways, of course!

89 Magic Square

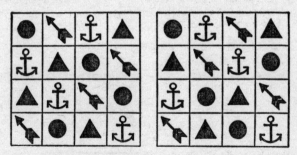

Here are the two solutions. A possible line of attack is to fill in the top and bottom rows. There are two other possibilities apart from those shown above. Then fill in, say, the other two circles so that only one appears in each row, column and diagonal. Then fill in the remaining signs as necessary. The other two possibilities soon show themselves to be impractical to complete correctly.

90 Sock Burglar

(*a*) 4 socks. (*b*) 8 socks (i.e., all of them). (*c*) 3 socks.

If he wants green, the first two *might* be blue, so he must take two more.

If he wants blue, the first six *might* be green, so he must take two more.

If he wants any pair, the first two *might* be different, but the third one is bound to be the same as one of them.

91 Donkey Derby

Clover was first, The Moke was last.

We get these groupings:

From (a) and (e)		*From (b) and (d)*	
Clementine		Big-Ears	Clover
– – – – – – – – –		Brownie	Brownie
– – – – – – – – –		Clover *or*	Big-Ears
Eeyore		– – – – –	– – – –
The Moke		Carrots	Carrots

From (*c*) Daisy is placed sixth, and from (*f*) Big-Ears cannot be first. There are only eight donkeys, so the left-hand group and one of the two right-hand groups must dove-tail together.

Only one result fits all these conditions, giving the order:

1st	Clover
2nd	Brownie
3rd	Big-Ears
4th	Clementine
5th	Carrots
6th	Daisy
7th	Eeyore
8th	The Moke

92 Still More Triangles

(*a*) 16 and (*b*) 47 triangles.

The lettered chart will help to identify the different types of triangle:

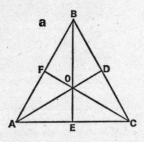 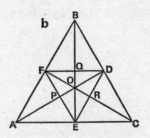

And here is a list of the triangles making up the totals shown:

	A B C	A B D	A B O	A F O	A F D	A F P	A F E	F D E
(*a*)	1	6	3	6	0	0	0	0
(*b*)	1	6	3	6	6	6	3	1

	F R E	F O E	F O P
(*a*)	0	0	0
(*b*)	6	3	6

93 Mixed Bag

9 Boothbars, 11 Boothchews and 50 Boothdrops.

This is one of those puzzles which comes out simply with the help of a little Algebra. However, 'trial and error' will get there in the end.

Consider first the Drops, which must (to avoid fractions of a penny) total 60 or 50 or 40 or 30 or 20 or 10; then the Bars, because they are the most expensive; and finally the Chews, keeping up to the total *cost*. You can draw up a table like this showing number of sweets possible (taking the case of 40 Drops as an example):

DROPS	BARS	CHEWS	Total	
40	11 (66p)	0	51	
(4p)	10 (60p)	6	56	
	9 (54p)	12	61	
	8 (48p)	18	66	
	7 (42p)	24	71	Oh bother, just missed!

Eventually you will find that there is only one possible solution.

94 Birthday Puzzle

John is now 15, James is 5.

Again, a little simple Algebra has this puzzle cracked open in no time, but trial and error will get there eventually.

Trial will soon show that John is now three times as old as James (their combined age is four times James' age or twice the difference, which itself is twice his age). For example, the ages could be 4 and 12, or 7 and 21.

Now the *difference* does not alter with age. The combined age will increase by this difference (from twice to three times the difference) so each brother's age will increase by half of it – which is by James' present age.

So James' age will double to 10, making him 5 now. His brother is now 15, three times as much.

(As a check, in 5 years time James will be 10, John will be 20, combined age 30, three times the difference of 10.)

95 Clockwise?

4 AM, 12 NOON, 8 PM

The 12-hour hand starts from the top at midnight, when the 24-hour hand is starting from the bottom towards it. The 12-hour hand travels twice as fast, because it makes two revolutions a day instead of one. So they first meet one-third of the way up from the bottom, that is at 4 AM (those geometrically minded would say that they meet 120° round from the top, 60° from the bottom).

They next meet at the top of the dial at noon (the 12-hour hand having travelled through 240° to the other hand's 120°).

Finally, they meet at the 8 o'clock position at 8 PM (having again travelled through 240° and 120°).

This process is now repeated for the next day. Here is the picture showing the angles travelled through:

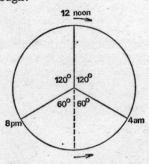

96 Repeater

9 minutes past six, 22 minutes past six, 12 minutes to seven.

Here are the chimes for these times:

Time	Hour chimes	Quarter chimes	Minute chimes	
6.09	6	0	9	
6.22	6	2	7	(6.15 + 7 minutes)
6.48	6	6	3	(6.45 + 3 minutes)

97 Puppies

PUPPIES WHICH PLAY WITH KANGAROOS DO NOT HAVE A LOUD BARK (*or* no puppy with a loud bark plays with kangaroos).

This conclusion is arrived at as follows:

All puppies which play with kangaroos have black noses (*b*),
– which means they have floppy ears (*e*),
– which means they chase cats (*c*),
– which means they are teachable (*a*),
– which means they do not have a loud bark (*d*).

98 Yacht Race

Second leg, South-South-East. Third leg, West-North-West.

At the second buoy yachts turn through 90° clockwise (sorry – to starboard!). At the third buoy the turn (also clockwise) is through 135°, that is half a revolution less 45°. It looks like this on the Mariner's Compass:

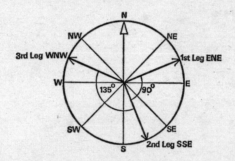

99 How's That Again?

She said, 'He said "What?".'

100 Calling the Cows Home

Ann-Win-Win (The farmer seems to assume the calf will be female!)

A numbering system with three names (Win, Ann and Jo) suggests one based on 'Scale 3', that is just using the numerals 0, 1 and 2. This is reinforced by the fact that numbers up to 8 need only single or double number-names, while number 9 needs a triple one. So we have:

1. Ann   4. Ann-Ann (11)   7. Jo-Ann (21)
2. Jo   5. Ann-Jo (12)   8. Jo-Jo (22)
3. Ann-Win (10)   6. Jo-Win (20)

where the numbers in brackets are in 'Scale 3' instead of the normal 'Scale 10'.
 This system would continue:

 9. Ann-Win-Win (100)   12. Ann-Ann-Win (110)   then Ann-Jo-Win (120)
10. Ann-Win-Ann (101)   13. Ann-Ann-Ann (111)   for 15, and so on.
11. Ann-Win-Jo (102)   14. Ann-Ann-Jo (112)

If the farmer is planning to have more than 26 cows in his herd he will have to introduce *quadruple* names, such as Ann-Win-Win-Win (1000) for 27!

Somehow, I don't believe this was quite what the farmer's wife had in mind, do you?

For those who enjoy teasers, here are some more
Beaver puzzle books:

Animal Quiz A Beaver original. Johnny Morris, universally known
and loved for his television programme *Animal Magic*, has created a
picture quiz book about all sorts of animals, fish and birds, full of fun
and facts for all the family

Picture Puzzles A Beaver original. Ninety-six pages packed with a
variety of brain-teasers, including mazes, 'spot-the-difference' and 'I spy'
games, written and illustrated by Walter Shepherd

Travel Quiz A Beaver original. A brain-teasing quiz book for all the
family on all aspects of travel by plane, train and car; by John Meirion

What's the Answer? A Beaver original. A mixed bag of puzzles using
numbers, words and pictures, and all fun to try

More Beaver Books

We hope you have enjoyed this Beaver Book. Here are some of the other titles:

The Pool of Fire The last book of John Christopher's 'Tripods' trilogy, which brings to a dramatic climax the story of the struggle to overthrow the Masters, invaders from outer space. The first two books are *The White Mountains* and *The City of Gold and Lead*, both published in Beavers

The Beaver Book of Games A Beaver original. George and Cornelia Kay describe dozens of games to play indoors and outdoors, including all the old favourites plus lots of new ones. Illustrated by Robin Anderson

Twelve Great Black Cats and Other Eerie Scottish Tales Ten weird and ghostly stories with a Scottish setting; by Sorche Nic Leodhas with illustrations by Michael Jackson

Battles and Battlefields David Scott Daniell brings to life fifteen of the most important battles fought in Britain between 1066 and 1746; with strategic maps and other illustrations by William Stobbs

Time's Delights A Beaver original. A collection of poems old and new about all aspects of time, chosen by Raymond Wilson, with enchanting illustrations by Meg Rutherford

New Beavers are published every month and if you would like the *Beaver Bulletin* – which gives all the details – please send a large stamped addressed envelope to:

Beaver Bulletin
The Hamlyn Group
Astronaut House
Feltham
Middlesex TW14 9AR

313964